This book belongs to:

Anahita

Rasoolpoor

Written by Jillian Harker

Illustrated by Rachael O'Neill

This edition published by Parragon in 2009

Parragon
Queen Street House
4 Queen Street
Bath BA1 1HE, UK

ISBN 978-1-4075-6808-9

Printed in China

Please!
Thank You!

PaRragon

Bath New York Singapore Hong Kong Cologne Delhi Melbourne

Mind your child's manners!

It's important to start teaching good manners early so that they become a habit for life. The stories in the **MIND YOUR MANNERS!** series are written to make learning good manners a positive experience.

Here are some of the ways you can help to make it fun:

* Find a quiet time to look at this story together and encourage your child to join in. The rhymes make the story easy to remember.

* After every question, talk about what you might say or do. Ask your child for suggestions. Joining in will help them to learn.

* Use the pages at the end of the story to check that your child understands when it is appropriate to use good manners.

* Throughout the day, reward your child's good manners with plenty of praise.

When you want to join in.
What do you say?
Do you cry and shout.
"I want to play!"?

That
can't
be
right!
It isn't
polite!

There's no need to be rude.
Here's the right thing to do -

First you say, "Please!"

And then say, "Thank you!"

"Here we go round
the mulberry bush!"

If you're hot and you're thirsty
And want an ice cream.
Is the right way to get one
To stamp 'round and scream?

That can't be right!
It isn't polite!

There's no need to be rude.
Here's the right thing to do -

First you say, "Please!"

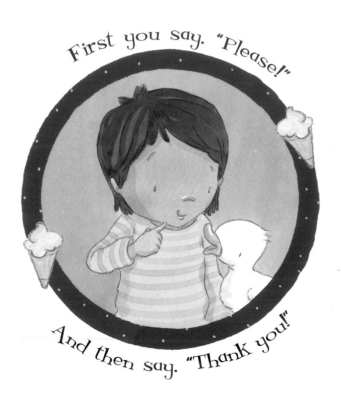

And then say, "Thank you!"

Yum, Yum!

If you need some help
To pedal along.
Do you say. "Push harder.
You're doing it wrong!"?

That
can't
be
right!
It isn't
polite!

There's no need to be rude.
Here's the right thing to do -

First you say. "Please!"

And then say. "Thank you!"

If you fly your kite
But it gets stuck in a tree.
Do you say, "Get my kite -
It's too high for me!"

That can't be right!
It isn't polite!

There's no need to be rude.
Here's the right thing to do -

First you say. "Please!"

And then say. "Thank you!"

If you want to be good
And have friends to play.

Remember your manners –
It's better that way!

There's no need to be rude.
You know what to do -

First we say, "Please!"

And then say, "Thank you!"

What will you say?

When you want to join in. what will you say?

If you said "Please". you were right!

When you are given an ice cream. what will you say?

If you said "Thank you". you were right!

Did you say "Please" or "Thank you" in all the right places?
Then give yourself a star!

When you want some help.
what will you say?

If you said "Please". you were right!

When you get help.
what will you say?

If you said "Thank you". you were right!